SCIENCE Q&A

COMMUNICATION

— Janice Parker —

Weigl Publishers Inc.

Published by Weigl Publishers Inc.
350 5th Avenue, Suite 3304, PMB 6G
New York, NY 10118-0069

Website: www.weigl.com

Library of Congress Cataloging-in-Publication Data

Parker, Janice.
 Communication / Janice Parker.
    p. cm. -- (Science Q/A)
 Includes index.
 ISBN 978-1-60596-066-1 (hard cover : alk. paper) -- ISBN 978-1-60596-067-8 (soft cover : alk. paper)
 1. Telecommunication--Miscellanea--Juvenile literature. I. Title.
 TK5102.4.P34 2010
 621.382--dc22

                                2009008349

Printed in China
1 2 3 4 5 6 7 8 9 0 13 12 11 10 09

Project Coordinator
Heather C. Hudak

Design
Terry Paulhus

Photo credits
Weigl acknowledges Getty Images as its primary image supplier for this title.

Every reasonable effort has been made to trace ownership and to obtain permission to reprint copyright material. The publishers would be pleased to have any errors or omissions brought to their attention so that they may be corrected in subsequent printings.

CONTENTS

What is Communication?

Communication refers to the various ways we send and receive messages. The messages can be in the form of writing, sounds, pictures, or video. Writing letters, publishing newspapers, and broadcasting television programs are just few of the ways we communicate with each other. Science has developed ways that allow us to communicate more easily and quickly. New jobs are created as new methods of communication are invented. Today, contacting other people or receiving current news is as easy as picking up a telephone or turning on a television or a computer. This ease of communication helps us feel closer to people all over the world. New devices and methods of communication, such as satellites and the Internet, have changed the way we interact with one another.

How did printing improve communication?

Long ago, speech and gestures were the only forms of communication. Stories and information were passed by word-of-mouth.

■ The most common printing process is offset printing. An inked image is transferred from a plate to a rubber blanket, then to the printing surface.

An important change happened when people began to write things down, first on clay, then on **papyrus**, and finally on paper. At first, anything on paper had to be handwritten. Whole books were handwritten until printing presses were invented. Printing, using a machine to place words and pictures on paper, is one form of communicating. If someone wanted ten copies of the same book, for example, he or she had to write out each of the books. This took a long time. Few people could read, and even fewer people owned books.

Printing allows people to make many copies of the same words or stories. The first printed pages were made in China by carving words and pictures into blocks of wood. The surface of the wood was covered with ink and the block was pressed down on a piece of paper. By adding more ink to the wood block, many copies of the same words and pictures could be made. The first printed book was made in this way around AD 868.

Ready...Type-Set...Go!

Typesetting means combining letters to make entire pages of words, or text. Today, computers are used for typesetting, so anyone can type and print out letters and other documents.

How did airplanes change the mail system?

Compared to some new forms of communication, delivering letters by mail seems slow to us today.

The mail system was once much slower than it is now. Using airplanes to send mail to different places around the world considerably reduced delivery time. At first, people had to travel many miles on foot to deliver a letter. The Pony Express used horses to carry letters.

The invention of trains and automobiles sped up mail delivery. Mail could be carried by vehicle to another city, or sometimes to another country. Trains and cars were not very fast, however, so mail took many days to travel from one place to another. When letters were carried by ships across the ocean, it could take many months before they reached their destination.

"Airmail" means sending mail to other parts of the world by airplane. The use of airmail changed the postal system forever. When you use airmail, it takes only hours or a few days for a package or letter to travel across the country or around the world.

Airplanes were invented in the early 1900s but were used to deliver mail several years later. Today, mail traveling great distances usually spends some time on an airplane.

■ Even with the rise of text messaging and email, the U.S. post office still handles 500 to 600 million pieces of mail each year.

Flights of Fantasy

The first airmail flight delivered postcards across India in 1911. Early airmail flights were often difficult for the pilot because there was very little room in the airplane for the mail. The first airmail pilot in the United States carried a bag of letters on his lap as he flew.

What is a telegraph?

The first telegraphs were invented in the early 1800s in Great Britain and the United States. Before the telegraph, messages had to be written and delivered by mail or by hand.

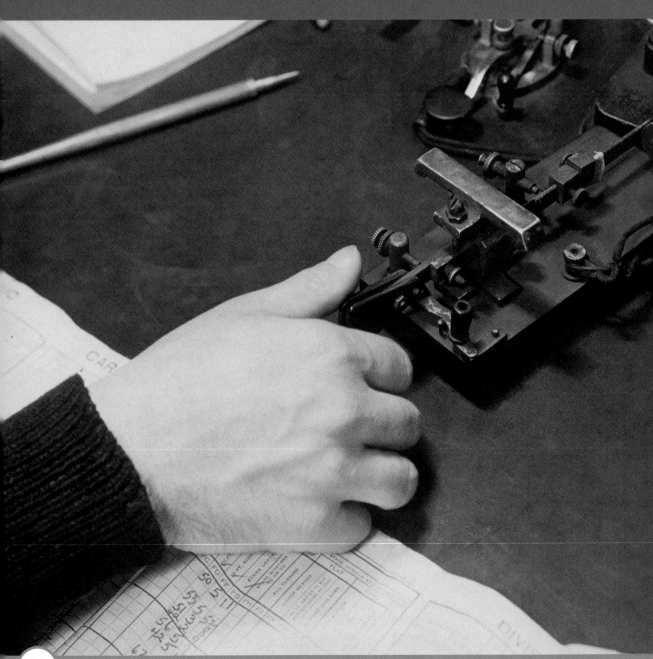

A telegraph is a machine that uses electricity to send messages along wires. Telegraph messages are sent by turning electricity on and off. Short bursts of electrical currents are sent along wires to the receiving telegraph. The receiver has magnetic needles on a dial with the letters of the alphabet written on it. Separate wires and coils act as electromagnets and control each needle. The currents from the sending machine create strong magnetic energy in the coil. As each letter is sent, the magnetic energy makes the needle point to that letter on the dial. This device was later improved to need only two needles.

In 1844, Samuel Morse invented a telegraph that made it even easier and quicker to send messages by telegraph. He developed a code, later named the Morse Code. Each letter or number is represented by a series of dots and dashes. Dots are created by short bursts of electricity, while dashes are created by longer bursts.

Like all telegraphs, a Morse telegraph is made up of two parts — a sender and a receiver. An operator uses a switch to tap out short or long electrical currents. At the other end, a receiver reads the currents as dots or dashes. The receiver prints the message out on a long piece of paper. The telegraph operator receiving the message then translates the Morse Code back into English.

■ In International Morse Code, a dot is made by pressing the telegraph key switch down and allowing it to spring back again rapidly. To make a dash, the key is held down for a longer period, letting it spring back more slowly.

S.O.S.

In 1999, a new satellite-based system replaced the Morse Code as the method for sending distress calls at sea. Anyone on a ship in trouble can press one button to send out the ship's identification number and its exact location.

How does a telephone work?

A telephone allows us to communicate with our voices rather than by dots and dashes.

find it quick

Learn more about the inventor of the telephone at **www.surfnetkids.com/ alexander_graham_bell.htm**.

Telephones have two parts: a mouthpiece and an earpiece. We speak into the mouthpiece and listen to the earpiece.

The sound waves from your voice are converted into electric current by the transmitter. A carbon transmitter uses a diaphragm, a thin metal disk, and a cup of carbon grains to send signals. The sound waves make the diaphragm vibrate. As it vibrates, it puts pressure on the carbon grains. Electric current flows through the grains. The current copies the pattern of vibrations and sends them to the receiver.

A foil-electret transmitter uses an electrically charged plastic diaphragm with a metal coating on one side. An electric field is created between the diaphragm and a hollow metal disk called a backplate. The vibrations caused by sound waves change the electric field, and the current becomes a copy of the speaker's sound waves.

The receiver, a metal disk in a flexible frame, changes electricity back into sound. It is surrounded by a ring-shaped permanent magnet. Another magnet, called an electromagnet, is attached to the other side of the diaphragm. When electricity from the sender's message flows through the electromagnet's coil, it becomes magnetized. The magnets pull in different directions and cause vibrations. This creates sound waves that are the same as those sent through the telephone.

Telephones use wires or cables to send their messages. Most telephones have a cable that leads to a nearby telephone exchange. When we make a telephone call, our call is connected by cables to the exchange. At the exchange, the call is directed to the area we are calling. A long-distance call to another country will first be sent by cables or optical fibers to an international exchange.

Telephone cables are buried under the ocean floor to connect continents. Radio waves and satellites are also used to send telephone calls.

That Rings A Bell!

We need to use area codes whenever we dial a long-distance number. Area codes connect us to the telephone exchange in the area we are calling.

What is fiber optics?

In the 1980s, scientists found that television cables could carry information better than the copper wires used in telephone lines. They wanted to increase the number of signals that telephone lines and computer networks could receive. They turned to fiber optics.

find it quick

Learn more about fiber optics at
www.explainthatstuff.com/fiberoptics.html.

A

■ Signals travel along fibers better than metal wires.

In fiber optics, light waves are changed into electric pulses, and sound is produced when these pulses vibrate through a speaker.

Each fiber has three parts: an inner core of reflective glass or plastic, a middle layer of glass called cladding, and an outside covering of plastic. When light hits the cladding, it reflects back into the core. Light waves travel down the length of a hollow fiber optics cable. Light waves can bend around curves. This makes it possible for one ray of light to travel farther. A device called an encoder measures these waves of light into a series of "on" and "off" pulses. The pulses can be translated into video, computer, or voice data.

A cable may contain one fiber, but there are often dozens of fibers bundled together in the center of the cable. Cables with one fiber carry only one wave of light, so they are faster than cables with multiple fibers.

Grand Strand

A fiber optic strand is about the same thickness as a single human hair. One strand can carry close to 2,000 telephone calls at one time.

How do fax machines work?

While telephones send voice messages through telephone lines, fax machines send written words and pictures.

Fax is short for facsimile, which means "copy." Fax machines send an exact copy of what is on a piece of paper, through phone lines, to another fax machine. This means that handwriting, illustrations, and even photographs can be sent by fax.

Both the sender and the receiver must have a fax machine or a computer with the software that enables receiving faxes. A fax machine divides a page into thousands of tiny squares. Each square is turned into a unique sound signal, depending on the darkness or lightness of the square. When the signals reach the receiving fax machine, they are turned back into squares. The fax machine then prints out a copy of what the original fax looked like. Sending a fax is as quick as making a phone call.

Alexander Bain invented the first fax machine. It consisted of a pendulum that made an electric signal to another pendulum in sync with the first that then transmitted the signal to chemically treated paper.

■ Some fax machines can make photocopies, scan documents into a computer, or print computer documents. They often have telephone and answering machine features.

Fax Facts

Fax machines were invented in the early 1900s, but they were not commonly used until the 1980s, when they became less expensive.

What are electromagnetic waves?

The discovery of electromagnetic waves in the 19th century led to a new form of communication.

Electromagnetic waves allow messages to be sent without using cables or wires. They are electrical and magnetic vibrations that travel through the air.

Electromagnetic waves are rays of electrical energy that exist in wave shapes in space. Like waves in water, electromagnetic waves have high points called crests, and low points called troughs. A **wavelength** is the length of a wave from one crest to the next. There are many different types of electromagnetic waves. Ultraviolet rays, which can cause sunburn, are one type. Infrared, Gamma, and X-ray waves are other types. Radio waves, which are used to send messages, have the longest wavelength of all electromagnetic waves. Some radio waves can travel over a distance as long as 6,250 miles (10,000 km).

Radio waves can be sent over short distances or even into outer space. Radio signals travel at the speed of light. Different types of radio waves are used for different purposes. Most radio broadcasts use long or medium-length radio waves. Short-wave radio signals are used for communication across great distances.

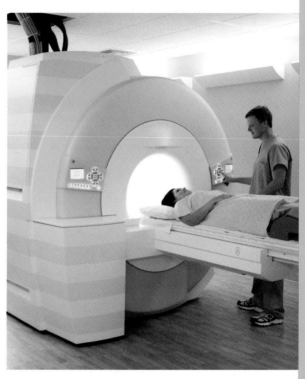

Magnetic resonance imaging (MRI) is a technique that uses a magnetic field and radio waves to create images of the head and body. Doctors use clear images to identify and diagnose a wide range of conditions.

Speed of Light

Electromagnetic waves travel at the speed of light. This is 186,282 miles (299,792 km) per second. The most basic electromagnetic wave is called a plane wave. It moves in a straight line.

What is radio?

Radio is a way to communicate by using electromagnetic waves instead of wires. The waves can carry sounds, such as human voices, across long distances.

find it quick

Learn more about the working of the radio at
www.gordon.army.mil/ocos/rdiv/ForKids/radowork.asp.

The first radio communication signals were sent by a man named Guglielmo Marconi in 1895. Marconi experimented with radio waves when he was a young man in Italy. He began to send radio waves through the air. Marconi created more powerful telegraph equipment that could send and receive radio signals over longer distances. He was able to send messages in Morse Code over distances of 2 miles (3.2 km). When Marconi moved to England in 1899, he succeeded in sending radio signals across the English Channel.

A couple of years later, Marconi sent radio signals from England to eastern Canada. Other scientists did not think it was possible to send radio waves so far because the Earth is round, and the waves would have to curve around it. Certain types of radio waves can reflect from a layer of the Earth's atmosphere.

This allows them to travel around the curve of the Earth.

Soon, radio communication was used by ships at sea. Before radio, ships could only send messages to other ships if they could see one another.

■ The face of communication was changed when telegraph equipment was invented.

Radio Gaga

There are two kinds of radio transmissions —amplitude modulation, or AM, and **frequency** modulation or FM. AM has lower frequencies than FM. FM has some advantages over AM signals. FM is relatively static-free in thunderstorms and other forms of interference. AM is not. FM also reproduces sound more accurately than AM.

What is two-way radio?

Most radios can only receive signals, not send them. Two-way radio allows people to both send and receive messages.

find it quick

Learn about ham radios at **www.electronics. howstuffworks.com/ham-radio1.htm.**

■ Hand-held radios are often called walkie-talkies or handie-talkies.

In some areas of the world, there are few or no telephone lines or exchanges. Two-way radio allows people in these areas to talk to one another. It is also used by airplane pilots. The pilots keep in contact with air traffic controllers at airports to find out when it is safe to take off and land. Police, ambulance workers, and firefighters all use two-way radio to stay in contact.

Truck drivers and others use a type of two-way radio, called citizen's band or CB radio, to talk to each other. CB radio allows truckers to warn other drivers of weather or road problems. It is also a way to help pass the time during long trips. CB radio can only be used over very short distances.

Amateur, or ham, radios are another way to communicate. They allow people to pick up and send radio signals around the world. Many people use amateur radios as a hobby. These radios also allow people to communicate during emergencies, when telephone lines are not working.

Over and Out!

People use a special language when speaking by CB radio. "Ten-four" means that they heard and understood the other person's message. "Over" signals the other person to reply, and "out" means no reply is necessary and the conversation has finished.

How do cellular telephones work?

Cellular telephones, also called mobile phones or cell phones, are not connected to telephone exchanges by wires or cables. Cell phones are a combination of a telephone and a two-way radio.

find it quick

Learn more about cell phones at **www.electronics. howstuffworks.com/cell-phone1.htm**.

Like most telephones, a cell phone changes voices into electrical currents. Instead of sending the currents along cables, cell phones send waves through the air. These waves are picked up by antennas on a receiving and transmitting station.

Receiving and transmitting stations are spread out across an area. Each receives radio signals sent out from a smaller area called a cell. Every cell works on a different frequency than its surrounding cells. Cells in one area are all linked to one central computer. If you are moving through an area while using your cell phone, the computer will automatically switch your call to the nearest transmitter.

■ Cell phones have changed a great deal over the years. In addition to making basic phone calls, mobile phones can be used for text messaging, emails, access to the Internet, gaming, and taking pictures.

Here is your challenge!

Make your own mobile phone. Punch a small hole in the bottom of two cans—just large enough to fit a string through. From the outside, insert one end of the string into the hole on one can and tie a few knots on the inside so it will not slip back out. Do the same to the other end of the string using the other tin can. Have a friend hold one can and walk away until the string is tight. Hold the can to your mouth and speak into it while the other holds the other can up to his or her ear. He or she should be able to hear what the other said if the string is tightened.

How have satellites improved communication around the world?

A satellite is an instrument that orbits Earth. Communication satellites pick up radio waves transmitted from Earth and bounce them back to other locations on Earth.

find it quick

Learn more about artificial satellites at www.spaceplace.nasa.gov/en/kids/goes/goes_poes_orbits.shtml.

It is sometimes difficult to send radio signals over long distances. The waves can have problems traveling over hills and mountains. The round shape of the Earth also makes it difficult to send waves. To travel around the curve of Earth, waves have to bounce off the ionosphere, a layer in the sky that reflects waves back down to Earth. Communication satellites, sometimes called comsats, make it easy to send signals around the world.

The first communication satellite was sent into space in 1960. This satellite, called Echo I, was shaped like a huge metal ball. It reflected weak microwave signals back to Earth. A more powerful communication satellite, Telstar, was sent into orbit in 1962. Telstar worked very well and communicated with transmitting and receiving stations in the United States and Great Britain.

■ The ionosphere is a region of charged particles in Earth's upper atmosphere.

Don't Hang Up!

Most long-distance telephone calls use a system of satellites called *intelsat*. Intelsat stands for International Telecommunications Satellite Organization. It has about 15 satellites in orbit around the Earth.

How does television work?

Television is similar to radio, but it uses pictures as well as sounds to communicate.

find it quick

Learn more about the birth of television at www.videouniversity.com/farnhal.htm.

A

Television became popular in the 1950s.

Television turns sound and pictures into electrical signals. These signals are sent into the air as radio waves. A receiver in your television turns the signals back into sound and pictures.

A television signal starts when light from the scene being filmed enters the camera. The camera changes the light into electric signals. A microphone picks up the sound and changes those waves into electric signals at the same time. These signals are then sent to the television receiver. The receiver makes sense of the signals and then changes them back into copies of the light and sound waves recorded by the camera. This is what we see on our television screens.

The first televisions were very large with small screens. When television was invented, there was only one channel to watch, and it only broadcast for a few hours a day. Only black-and-white images were available. Color television was invented in the 1960s. Color television signals are broken down into red, green, and blue light. These signals are changed back to the original colors in our television sets.

Perfect Ratio

The standard TV that has been around since the 1950s has a width to height ratio of 4:3. LCD flatscreen TVs have a ratio of 16:9. Super widescreens having a ratio of 2.35:1 are also available.

What are cable television and satellite television?

At first, cable television signals were sent through wires, or cables, that connected the cable television company to homes. Today, cable television companies also use communications satellites to transmit signals.

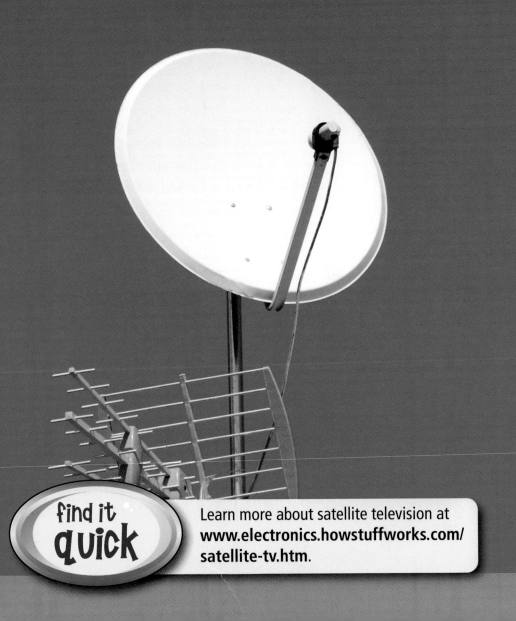

find it quick

Learn more about satellite television at **www.electronics.howstuffworks.com/satellite-tv.htm**.

Most television sets need antennae to receive television signals from local stations. Some homes and other buildings have television antennae on their roofs to pick up the signals. These antennae must be close to a local television station in order to pick up the signals. Cable television and satellite television allow us to receive signals from much farther away.

With technology changing fast, soon television antennae will not be needed with a direct-to-home telecast. To get cable television, you must go through a cable company. If you have your own satellite dish, you can get television signals from around the world without using a cable company. A satellite dish is a special type of antenna that receives signals directly from satellites in space. While you may only have access to a few local channels, there are hundreds of cable channels. There are even more channels available by satellite.

■ Satellite reception was launched during the 1980s. It is now being widely used across most of the world.

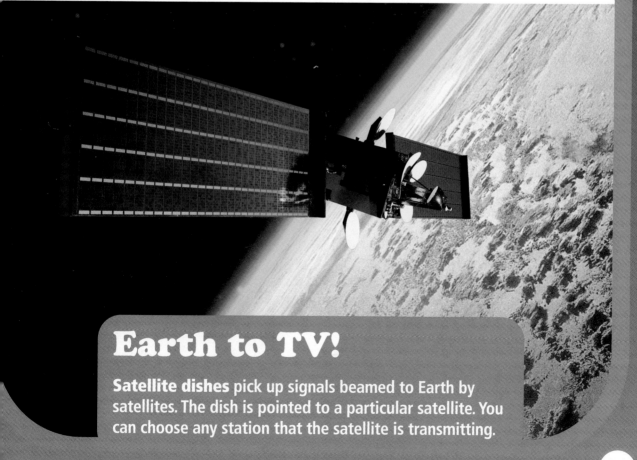

Earth to TV!

Satellite dishes pick up signals beamed to Earth by satellites. The dish is pointed to a particular satellite. You can choose any station that the satellite is transmitting.

What is noise pollution?

When we think of pollution, we usually think of problems that affect the land and air, such as garbage or smog caused by automobiles. However, there are some kinds of pollution, such as noise pollution, that cannot be seen.

Noise pollution can be annoying. It is very difficult to work or sleep if you are surrounded by loud noise. Noise pollution can also be dangerous. Very loud noises can cause hearing loss. Even lesser noises can damage our eardrums if we listen to them long enough.

Both radios and televisions are designed to make very loud sounds. Many people wear headsets, which are earphones attached to a headband, to listen to radios or television. Headsets allow us to listen without bothering the people around us, but listening to loud music or television through a headset can also damage our hearing.

■ A pneumatic drill, or jackhammer, is used to drill rock and break up pavement.

Sounds are measured in decibels. A whisper is about 30 decibels, while normal conversation is about 60 decibels. A jackhammer is 130 decibels. Long exposure to any noise above 90 decibels, such as a lawn mower, can cause hearing loss. Most governments have made laws to protect people from noise pollution. Such laws may not allow sound over a certain level during the night, so people can sleep. They also may not allow loud noises in neighborhoods where many people live.

Here is your challenge!

Walk around your neighborhood, and listen hard for different sounds such as cars, trucks, birds, dogs, and lawn mowers. You may be so used to the noises that you do not notice them anymore. Make recordings of any sounds that you think are noise pollution. Is your neighborhood too loud? Think about the types of noises that bothered you the most. Then, see if you can do anything to reduce noise. You could start from your own home.

How are sounds and pictures digitized?

Digitization means changing pieces of information, such as sounds and images, into digital information. Digital information is all of the same information carried by electrical signals changed into **binary code**.

find it quick

See how sounds and pictures are digitized at www.cs.cf.ac.uk/Dave/Multimedia/node145.html.

Computers have led to a new communication technology called digitization. Binary code is the system that is used to run all computers and electronics. Binary numbers are a series of the numbers 0 and 1.

In the binary system, an electrical current is either on (1) or off (0). Binary numbers can be put together in different combinations called binary codes. Binary codes can represent numbers, letters, pictures, and sounds.

■ A microchip or silicon chip is a mini electronic circuit made up mainly of semiconductor devices.

Digitized information has much better sound and picture quality than other systems, such as radio waves. Also, many digital signals can be sent along a single wire at the same time. Computers easily store and send digital information. Computers store information on their hard drive. They send information through a network or over a modem.

Digitize This

Digital television converts sounds and images electronically into binary code. Digital television transmitters do not need to send the information contained in every picture frame. Only the changes from frame to frame are sent. This means that the information can be sent more quickly, and that more than one signal can be sent over a single cable. Digital television will allow us to have access to even more television stations than ever.

How do computers talk to one another?

In order for people to communicate using computers, the machines must be linked to each other through a common network.

Local Area Network

Wide Area Network

Computer information travels by wires or optical fibers.

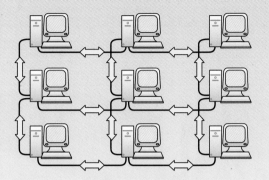

Computer information is translated by a modem and travels to other modems.

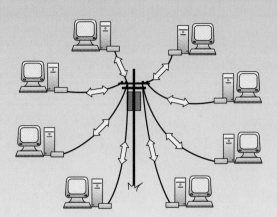

A computer network is a connection between two or more computers. It allows digital information to be sent quickly from computer to many other computers. Through a network, a computer can send messages to other computers almost anywhere in the world.

There are two types of computer networks: Local Area Networks (LANs) and Wide Area Networks (WANs). Computers in one office or building can be connected by wires or optical fibers in a LAN.

Computers in different buildings or even different countries are linked into a WAN by telephone lines. This is done using a device called a modem, which changes computer information into signals that can travel along telephone lines. Modems change digital information into electrical signals. These signals are transferred over telephone lines to other modems connected to computers.

Bit by Bit

Modem speed is measured in bits, or tiny pieces of information, per second. Fast modems can send thousands of words and other information in a few seconds.

What is the Internet?

The Internet, sometimes called the Net, is the largest computer network in the world.

find it quick

Learn more about the Internet at
www.bcls.lib.nj.us/Classes/Intforkids.

■ An Internet café, or cybercafé, is a place where people can use a computer with Internet access. The concept of a cybercafé was invented in 1994 by Ivan Pope.

People around the world are connected to the Internet through their computers. The Internet is like a large network made up of many smaller networks. Common methods of internet access include dial-up, landline, T- lines, **Wi-Fi**, satellite, and cell phones.

The Internet began in 1969. At first it was used only by the United States military. Soon it was also used to send mail electronically. Governments, universities, and businesses began to exchange messages and information over the Internet. Most people did not use the Internet at first because very few people had a computer at home. In the 1980s, the development of small, inexpensive personal computers (PCs) meant that more people could afford a computer. They could also connect to the Internet.

The Internet allows people to send messages around the world quickly and cheaply. We can also use the Internet to find information on almost any topic.

One in a Million

Millions of pieces of information pass through the Internet every second.

How is the World Wide Web different from the Internet?

The Internet is a worldwide network of computers. The World Wide Web is mostly used on the Internet.

find it quick

Learn more about the birth of the Internet at www.learnthenet.com/english/html/01birth.htm.

The Internet connects millions of users across the world. The World Wide Web is a way to find information on the Internet.

The Web is made up of millions of web pages. Web pages contain information in many forms, including words, pictures, sounds, and even video. The Web uses **hyperlinks** to travel from one web page to another. Hyperlinks or URLs are pictures or underlined words that are connected to other sites or documents on the Web. Underlined words are called hypertext. When you click on a hyperlink or URL, you are taken to a different

■ Uniform Resource Locators, or URLs, are the addresses used to locate the files on the World Wide Web.

web page. Along with electronic mail (e-mail), the Web is the most popular part of the Internet.

The World Wide Web is very easy to use if you have an Internet connection and a browser. A browser is a computer program that helps people move around the Web. **Search engines**, programs that help people find specific web pages, allow people to search for web pages on any chosen subjects.

The whole world at your fingertips

The World Wide Web was created in 1989 in Switzerland. The first web browsers could only view words, not pictures. The first graphical web browser appeared in 1993. Some of the Web browsers currently available for personal computers include Internet Explorer, Mozilla Firefox, Safari, Netscape, and AOL Explorer.

What is electronic mail?

Electronic mail, or e-mail, is a way of sending messages over the Internet. E-mail is the fastest way to send a written letter. Once a message is typed out and sent, it takes only seconds to reach another computer anywhere in the world.

find it quick

Learn about e-mail communication at **www.howstuffworks.com/email.htm**.

mail server

Sender's computer directs e-mail message to recipient's mail server.

Server forwards message to recipient's computer.

tim@mycity.com

jane@myaddress.com

Recipient can reply to the sender or forward the sent message to other recipients.

mail server

Before e-mail, it was not as easy to send messages to people who lived far away. E-mail is both quick and inexpensive. You can e-mail someone in another country and receive an answer from them right away.

When you send an e-mail message, your computer directs it to a computer called a mail server. That computer then sends your message to the proper e-mail address. Your letter gets stored in the receiver's electronic mailbox until he or she opens it. This process can take seconds, even if the message is being sent across the world.

Getting an e-mail address is simple. Online services like web portals and **Internet Service Providers** offer e-mail. You create a user name and password, which allows you to access your mailbox and send messages. This is called an e-mail account. Even people who do not own computers can use e-mail. Accounts can be set up for free on the Internet. Many groups and libraries allow people to use computers to send and receive e-mail. E-mail helps people communicate quickly and easily with friends and relatives. It can be used to send more than simple letters. With proper equipment and software, pictures, sounds, video clips, and even computer programs can be sent via the Internet.

Here is your challenge!

Emoticons, commonly called smileys, are special characters that express emotions and expressions within an e-mail. When turned sideways, they represent a face. For example, a colon, dash, and right bracket, :-), is a smile. Abbreviations are commonly used in e-mail messages to save time typing. Research emoticons and try creating some of your own.

Communication Careers

Webmasters and Web Designers

Web designers and developers create web pages for companies or individuals. The web developer makes sure the website includes all the information and features, such as photos and video, that the company wants to share with the public. Webmasters are the people who maintain web pages. The webmaster makes sure the company website is running smoothly. All of the information must be up-to-date, so the webmaster makes changes to the site as needed. He or she must also make sure that all e-mails or messages sent to the website are answered.

Electronic Technician

Electronic technicians work to build, install, or repair electrical equipment used for communicating. Electronic technicians work with equipment such as telephones, televisions, and computer networks. If telephone systems are not working, technicians repair the problem. They repair problems at telephone exchanges and repair the cables that connect computers, fax machines, and other electronic equipment. Advanced technology has created more opportunities for electronic technicians. The popularity of television, telephones, and the Internet means technicians are usually in demand in the communication industry.

find it quick

Learn more about electronic technicians and webmasters at **www.kids.gov/6_8/6_8_careers.shtml**.

Young scientists at work
How does a simple printing press work?

What You Need

A rubber eraser

A knife to cut the eraser

Two flat pieces of wood or stiff cardboard

Glue

Ink

Paper

What to Do

Ask an adult to help you cut the eraser into long, thin strips. Glue the strips on one of the boards to shape a word or words. The words and letters must all be backward. Carefully use a small paintbrush or ink pad to apply ink to the rubber letters pasted on the first board. Place the paper over your words. Put the second board over the paper. Press down evenly on the top board for several seconds. Remove the top board, and then carefully remove the paper. Your words should now be printed on the paper.

Take a science survey

How often do you use the different types of machines discussed in this book? We all use telephones. Most of us also have televisions at home and use computers at home or at school. You may not realize just how often you use these communication tools.

1. How many times do you use a telephone everyday? Every week?

2. How many telephones do you have in your home? Does anyone in your family have a cellular telephone?

3. Is there more than one television set in your home? How many are there?

4. How many hours of television do you watch everyday? Every week?

5. Do you have a computer? How often do you use it?

6. How many hours a week do you spend using the Internet at home and at school?

SURVEY RESULTS

There are 120 million telephones in the United States, more than in any other country. According to Reading Across America, an organization that offers programs that encourage young people to read, the average young person spends 30 hours a week watching TV or playing video games. By the time a child graduates from high school, he or she will have spent 20,000 hours in front of a television and only 13,000 in a classroom. The average American watches almost 50 hours of television a week. Most homes in the United States have a computer. About 59 percent of all households in the United States have access to the Internet.

46

Fast Facts

The more words a telegram contains, the more it costs to send it. People who send telegrams try to keep their messages short.

In Morse Code, the letters "SOS" are used to say that the sender of the message is in trouble. "SOS" was chosen because the letters were easy to remember: three dots stand for the letter "S," and three dashes for the letter "O."

Radio signals allow us to communicate with astronauts in space. Television images can also be beamed between Earth and a space shuttle.

The smallest television in the world is about the size of a wristwatch.

Every web page on the Internet has its own address, called a URL, or Uniform Resource Locator.

Fiber-optic cables are as thin as human hair, but they can transmit thousands of telephone calls at a time.

Many web pages on the Internet are written in a special type of programming language called HTML, which stands for Hyper Text Markup Language.

Space shuttles take satellites into space. Astronauts on space shuttle missions can capture and repair satellites in space.

Computer viruses are small programs designed to harm computer systems. They can be transmitted through the Internet.

The first printing press was similar to the presses used to make cider and olive oil.

Glossary

binary code: a system that breaks down information and stores it as combinations of the numbers 0 and 1

frequency: the number of times an electric wave vibrates each second

hyperlink: pictures or words on the World Wide Web that connect you to another web page with the click of a mouse

Internet service provider: a company that has large computers hooked into the Internet. Home and business users must connect to a service provider in order to have access to the Net

papyrus: an ancient writing material made from plants

satellite dish: a special antenna that can pick up radio waves reflected from satellites in space

search engines: programs on the World Wide Web that help people find certain web pages

wavelength: the distance between two points on a moving wave

Wi-Fi: a set of standards for transmitting data over a wireless network

Index

9110
6